RIVER MONSTERS

EXTREME FISHING

BIGGER, MEANER, FASTER!

ANIMAL PLANET

Thea Feldman, Editor and Writer
Swing Design, Design and Art Direction
Terri Fredrickson, Copy Editor
Greenfield Creative Consulting, Project Management
Kari Greenfield, Licensing

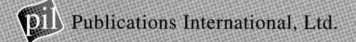

Published by
Louis Weber, C.E.O.
Publications International, Ltd.
7373 North Cicero Avenue
Lincolnwood, Illinois 60712

Ground Floor, 59 Gloucester Place
London W1U 8JJ
Customer Service:
1-800-595-8484 or customer_service@pilbooks.com

www.pilbooks.com

8 7 6 5 4 3 2 1

Manufactured in USA.

ISBN-13: 978-1-4508-4224-2
ISBN-10: 1-4508-4224-0

CONTENTS

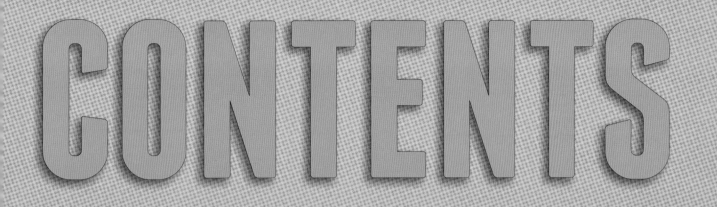

THEY'RE

Tribespeople in a tiny village tucked away in a dense jungle rain forest in Suriname recount stories of a mysterious murderous monster living in the nearby river. The creature has reportedly attacked and devoured a monkey unlucky enough to plunge into the water while trying to jump across it by swinging from overhead tree branches. The culprit is also accused of grabbing a hunting dog and ripping open its stomach. And villagers recall seeing reptiles and birds disappear in the water, snatched by something from below. People themselves have come under attack, sporting scars on hands and arms that tell of serious struggles with aquatic enemies.

What manner of monster is responsible? The answer to that question is exactly what Jeremy Wade, biologist, writer, lifelong fisherman, and host of the Animal Planet™ television series, *River Monsters*, set off to discover in one of his most extreme adventures ever.

Solving the mysteries of what lurks in fresh water is nothing new for Jeremy, who has spent 25 years investigating tales of river monsters and tracking down the animals that lie behind the stories. The vast majority of suspects have turned out to be fish. And many of these fish, it turns out, don't deserve their rotten reputations.

Jeremy takes a multifaceted approach to clearing a fish's name. He studies the fish's behavior and the conditions of the river the animal is living in. He also gathers information from local people and animal experts in order to understand why the interaction between the fish and other animals has seemingly taken an aggressive turn. And, of course, he goes out to hunt down the suspect so he can examine it up-close and personal before releasing it back to its watery home.

For the villagers of Suriname, it turns out that Wolf Fish can go on vicious attacks of people and other larger animals when there is not enough of their normal diet of other fish and other small animals, or if they find themselves cut off in pools of water without any food. Jeremy's investigation concluded with certainty that the Wolf Fish has the ability to be every bit as treacherous as the infamous predatory piranha.

"FOR AS LONG AS I CAN REMEMBER I'VE HAD A PASSION THAT BORDERS ON OBSESSION: DANGEROUS, FRESHWATER FISH HAVE GOT ME WELL AND TRULY HOOKED".

BITING!

Wolf Fish

Electric Eel

Short-Tailed River Stingray

Red-Bellied Pacu

Sawfish

THERE'S SOMETHING FISHY HERE

An aggressive Wolf Fish in Suriname. A high-voltage Electric Eel in Brazil. A venom-packing stingray in Argentina. A predatory Pacu in Papua New Guinea. A Sawfish with a chainsaw for a snout in Australia. A cute little goldfish swimming in a bowl on your desk. These vastly different animals are all fish. What does that mean? It means that each one has a backbone, fins for getting around, and gills for breathing in the water. These things make a fish a fish, whether it swims in freshwater rivers, lakes, streams, and ponds (or bowls) or in saltwater oceans and seas.

GOING TO THE EXTREME

NORTH AMERICA

EUROPE

SOUTH AMERICA

AROUND THE WORLD

When it comes to tracking down a river monster, there's nowhere on the planet too remote for Jeremy Wade. He has journeyed through dense jungles, ventured to villages that no outsiders have ever been to, trekked to remote hilltop locations, braved rugged frontiers, and so much more—all in pursuit of freshwater creatures alleged to be killers. He has faced extreme conditions, endured personal discomforts, and risked danger to life and limb to uncover the truth about what's really lurking in the world's rivers. His latest round of adventures has taken him into uncharted territories—to places he's never been before in search of river monsters the likes of which he's never encountered.

SURINAME
WOLF FISH
JUNGLE KILLER

BRAZIL
ELECTRIC EEL
ELECTRIC EXECUTIONER

ARGENTINA
SHORT-TAILED RAY
SILENT ASSASSIN

"RIVERS ARE OFTEN MURKY AND THE ONLY WAY TO FIND OUT WHAT IS REALLY THERE IS TO CAST A LINE INTO THE WATER—IT'S A BIT LIKE ASKING A QUESTION. AND THE ANSWER WHEN IT COMES CAN SOMETIMES BLOW YOU AWAY."

ASIA

AFRICA

AUSTRALIA

JAPAN
GIANT SALAMANDER
COLD-BLOODED HORROR

PAPUA NEW GUINEA
PACU
THE MUTILATOR

AUSTRALIA
SAWFISH
CHAINSAW PREDATOR

NEW ZEALAND
LONGFIN EEL
FLESH RIPPER

"A FISH WITH REAL NERVE GUIDED BY THE NOSE OF A BLOODHOUND AND ARMED WITH HUNDREDS OF PACKED TEETH."

FLESH RIPPER

Jeremy had always thought of New Zealand as a totally safe place to get into the water until he began hearing stories of a snakelike freshwater creature large and strong enough to kill a person. Because New Zealand has no snakes, Jeremy determined that the culprit was a Longfin Eel, a fish with a body like a serpent.

Knowing that eels are more active at night and that they rely on smell rather than sight to find food led Jeremy to his first stop: a dark cave on North Island where some eels have lived without daylight for at least 30 years. To tempt them out of the shadows he dangled meat in the water and immediately the fearless fish picked up the scent and appeared for a meal.

Appealing to the fish's extraordinary ability to sense blood, at his next location Jeremy successfully used a concoction of guts and <u>offal</u> to draw them in.

Jeremy traveled next to South Island, where some of the biggest eels mentioned in historical records had been caught in deep lakes in the interior. On remote Lake Manapouri, which reaches deeper than 1,500 feet at its middle, Jeremy and his guide, an expert eel fisherman, caught and released an impressive 16-pounder.

Intent on finding still larger Longfin Eels, Jeremy traveled to an even more remote backwater location that was swarming with hungry eels. To increase his chances of luring them in, Jeremy turned himself into human bait by donning an outfit soaked with fish guts. For protection he wore a thick wet suit and Kevlar® bite-proof gloves. Sticking close to the bank for a quick escape, he entered the water. Almost instantly he was surrounded by dozens of bold and ravenous eels, including one that bit the inside of his thigh and a 4-footer that bit his hand and held on even as Jeremy lifted his arm out of the water!

Jeremy emerged from his adventure unscathed and importantly, convinced that a pack of ravenous eels could "handily" devour a full-grown human being!

The island country of New Zealand is made up of two main islands, North Island and South Island, which have been separate from the rest of the world for 80 million years. Jeremy Wade traveled to some of the most remote bodies of freshwater in this remote place in search of a legendary flesh-eater.

LONGFIN EEL

Jeremy captures migrating eels by using channels he scooped out of the beach sand.

Giant eels slither across the rocky beach on their migratory route.

"WITH THIS ANIMAL IT ISN'T ABOUT SIZE— SLIP AND FALL OVER IN SOME LONELY RIVER AND IT'S THE HUNGRY PACK THAT CAN SEAL YOUR FATE."

LOCAL LORE

The Longfin Eel is a local legend among New Zealanders today. On the North Island folks tell the story of an eel with a massive head, 1 foot across, that rammed a diver with enough force to crack one of his ribs!

These super-size monsters have also been a prominent feature of Maori culture for centuries. The Maori, New Zealand's indigenous people, have many stories that show their respect for the adversarial eel. According to one legend, all eels sprang from a single, huge ancestor during a time when there was a drought up in heaven. A giant eel was sent down to Earth to try to find water for the gods but while there it tried to seduce the wife of Maui, the most powerful of the gods. Maui, enraged, fought with the eel and hacked it in two. The eel's severed head gave rise to all the seawater eels and the tail gave rise to all the freshwater eels, including the lethal Longfin.

THE BUSINESS END

Hundreds of teeth that point backward line the viselike jaws of this predatory fish. It is easy enough to imagine how a Longfin would firmly grip its prey and drag it under the water. But Jeremy needed to figure out how a fish with teeth designed to grab and hold its catch earned its repulsive reputation for cutting and ripping flesh.

Jeremy positioned a hunter's donated deer carcass in the water, surrounded by surveillance cameras. After two hours a pack of hungry eels descended upon the carcass. Each eel gripped the victim firmly and then spun itself violently around to twist off chunks of flesh!

FISH FACTS

LENGTH: Up to 8 feet
WEIGHT: Up to 55 pounds
This slithery swimmer is the largest of New Zealand's three species of freshwater eel. But its size and aggressive attitude are not the only things to fear about this fish. It has toxic blood coursing through its body deadly enough to kill a dog. A single splash of the potent poison in a person's eyes or on the lips can cause painful swelling for days. Three teaspoons, if ingested, is enough to be fatal!

PAPUA NEW GUINEA

Reports of an unidentified freshwater creature tearing chunks of flesh from unsuspecting fishermen spur Jeremy to take his first trip to the island of Papua New Guinea, which lies north of Australia where the Coral Sea meets the South Pacific. Even though people have lived on the land for more than 50,000 years, the landscape itself has changed little since prehistoric times.

RED-BEL

After 4 flights, 48 hours, and 9,000 miles, Jeremy arrived in Ambunti, in the remote northwest corner of the country. It is a place with steep-sided mountains and impenetrable forest. There are few roads in this part of the country. The Sepik River, which winds through the forest for 700 miles, is the main way to travel.

Months before his trip, knowing that the local people would not welcome unannounced visitors, Jeremy had arranged to stay for two weeks in a village deep in the heart of the forest. Once there he spoke with the villagers about the fish that had been terrorizing them. He learned from the village elders that only a handful of species lives in the river and they are not capable of making such aggressive attacks. So what kind of river monster was leaving humanlike bite marks in the legs of unsuspecting victims? And, according to the villagers, this was a fish ferocious enough not only to bite into human flesh but also fearless enough to attack crocodiles!

After ruling out crocodiles themselves as the culprit, Jeremy sought out the predatory fish using pork as bait. Quite a long time ago, when the local tribespeople were cannibalistic they reportedly thought that human flesh tasted like pork, so much so that they called it "long pig!"

Much to Jeremy's surprise he hooked a Red-Bellied Pacu, a fish he had caught before, but in the faraway Amazon River in South America. And the Pacu is a vegetarian fish in its native habitat. It turned out that in Papua New Guinea, the Pacu has developed not only a taste for pork but for people too.

THE MUTILATOR
LIED PACU

THE BUSINESS END

At first Jeremy thought the fish he was after couldn't be the Pacu, because a Pacu's teeth are designed for crushing and grinding the seeds and nuts that make up its normal vegetarian diet. But he soon realized that this fish's usual food was in short supply, which caused the Pacu to turn predatory. Now when they hear other fish splashing in the water these carnivorous creatures come quickly, with their teeth bared and ready to bite.

A tribesman holding a Pacu.

"IT'S ALL MUSCLE WITH SNAPPING JAWS."

CULTURE CONNECTION

Not only did Jeremy need to proceed carefully with the predatory fish and killer crocodiles in the Sepik River, but he also had to navigate a culture vastly different from any that he had previously encountered. The tribes that live along the Sepik are cut off from the outside world and have a culture steeped in superstitions, myths, and mystery. They are notoriously wary of outsiders, including other tribes. Tribes have their own languages and reportedly there are more than 700 different ones that are spoken! Pidgin is a language used to conduct trade, and allows various tribes to communicate with one another, and bits of English are being increasingly introduced and understood.

Rituals and traditional beliefs remain strong among the people. Many believe that river spirits are responsible for the mutilating attacks on people and they perform elaborate hypnotic dances in an attempt to appease the spirits. Powerful, menacing spirits are also thought to exist in the middle of the forest where Jeremy headed to fish.

FISH FACTS

LENGTH: Up to 3 feet
WEIGHT: Up to 55 pounds
The Red-Bellied Pacu is a cousin of the piranha family of fish, both commonly found swimming in the Amazon River in South America. So how did it wind up thousands and thousands of miles away from its usual home and in the Sepik River of Papua New Guinea? Villagers told Jeremy that Pacu had been introduced to the river about 15 years ago in order to give the local people enough to eat. What apparently happened, Jeremy reasoned, was that in the absence of large predatory fish to eat it, and with its normal vegetarian diet in short supply, the fish transformed themselves into flesh-eaters. They took over the river, upsetting its natural balance and becoming a deadly threat to humans.

JEREMY'S GIANTS

Unlike land animals, aquatic creatures have their bodies supported by water. This means gravity does not limit how massive they can become. And as long as there is enough food, if left undisturbed, there's no limit to how gigantic a fish can get. Jeremy has battled against and reeled in many of the world's most massive river monsters, including some creatures that are longer than he is tall and are many times heavier than he is!

Let's revisit some of Jeremy's toughest and most bruising encounters with some of the world's most formidable freshwater giants.

NUMBER 1

KALI RIVER MAN-EATER
GOONCH

Jeremy traveled to the Himalayan Mountain Range in India to catch this huge carnivorous beast accused of dragging children, adults, and even a water buffalo to their deaths underneath the currents of the murky Kali River. It took more than a month for Jeremy to reel in a Goonch, a sumo-size member of the catfish family. He knew instantly it could be capable of the murderous crimes it stood accused of.

FISH FACTS

LENGTH: Up to 6.5 feet
WEIGHT: More than 160 pounds

THIS WILL HOOK YOU

It is possible this man-eater grows fat on human corpses. It is the Hindu custom to burn the dead on the banks of rivers before putting their remains in the water, and catfish are notorious scavengers. So when the Goonch engages in gruesome gobbling, it is only doing what comes naturally.

"I'VE INVESTIGATED REPORTS OF MASSIVE FISH FROM ALMOST EVERY CONTINENT AND HAVE DISCOVERED FOR MYSELF THAT SOME UNDERWATER LEGENDS ARE MORE THAN JUST FISHERMEN'S TALL TALES."

LETHAL IMPACT
ARAPAIMA

These Amazon River monsters have hard heads and an unnerving habit of bursting out of the water like missiles. Jeremy discovered this for himself years earlier in Brazil when one delivered a bruising blow to his chest. A heart scan later showed that Jeremy had suffered permanent muscle damage similar to that caused by the steering wheel in a car crash! Jeremy's more recent rematch with the species was much more successful: None of the monsters' potentially punishing punches landed.

FISH FACTS

LENGTH: Up to 10 feet
WEIGHT: Up to 475 pounds

THIS WILL HOOK YOU

The Arapaima uses its hard head in defense. To kill prey, however, it sucks in its victim from a distance, then crushes it with its bony tongue!

NUMBER
2

17

MYSTERY OF THE GIANT LAKE MONSTER

WHITE STURGEON

Jeremy traveled far from his usual tropical fishing spots to the icy subartic of Alaska in search of an elusive and enormous river monster accused of pulling fishermen out of their boats. He determined that the culprit was the White Sturgeon, which can jump out of the water and knock people overboard. No one knows what makes a sturgeon jump, but there's no mistaking when it does!

FISH FACTS

LENGTH: Up to 20 feet
WEIGHT: Up to 1,800 pounds

THIS WILL HOOK YOU

The White Sturgeon has no teeth! Its mouth functions like a vast vacuum, sucking in fish and other food off the muddy river bottom.

"FOR A FEW MOMENTS THERE, I WAS ACTUALLY IN THE PRESENCE OF THE CREATURE THAT IS THE LAKE MONSTER"

FISH FACTS
LENGTH: Up to 10 feet
WEIGHT: More than 300 pounds

A MEDIEVAL KILLER RETURNS
WELS CATFISH

Introduced by a scientist into the River Ebro in Spain in 1974, the Wels Catfish quickly took to its new environment. The size of the river, the warm water temperature, and the plentiful supply of carp and other fish are all conducive to growing gargantuan river monsters. Jeremy caught one that was 7 feet 4 inches long, and he could hear an echo coming out of its massive mouth!

THIS WILL HOOK YOU
The Wels Catfish will only attack people if it feels threatened. That means you definitely don't want to be in the same water as a male protecting about 300,000 eggs that the female laid in aquatic plants.

GIANT FRESHWATER STINGRAY
A MONSTER IN OUR MIDST

One of Jeremy's toughest tug-of-war battles was with this terror of Thailand. A two-hour energy-sapping stalemate with one underwater opponent ended with Jeremy's rod snapping in half just as he was finally reeling in his killer catch. The rod wasn't the only thing that snapped—so did the tendons in Jeremy's right shoulder, which has left that arm permanently weakened. After "reloading" with a shorter rod, Jeremy succeeded in catching a 400-pound female stingray that took seven people to haul onto the shore, where she surprisingly gave birth to two live young!

THIS WILL HOOK YOU
This river monster Jeremy caught was armed with a deadly 10-inch, venom-coated, serrated barb on its whiplike tail!

FISH FACTS
Length: Up to 16 feet
Weight: More than 1,300 pounds
Wingspan: Up to 7 feet

A RIVER RUNS

More than 100 kinds of fish swim this American river, including some super-size species of catfish and sturgeon. Perhaps the most infamous Mississippi River monster is the Alligator Gar, which can be up to 10 feet long and tip the scales at a hefty 365 pounds.

EUROPE

NORTH AMERICA

· NORTH AMERICA ·
NUMBER · 1
MISSISSIPPI
LENGTH: AROUND
2,320 MILES

AFRICA

AROUND THE WORLD

Jeremy has tracked down freshwater river monsters wherever they swim—whether that is in a fast-flowing mighty river or a stagnant muddy freshwater pool that forms seasonally on a cattle ranch!

Many of Jeremy's destinations have been remote locations but more and more river monsters are making their way into waterways in heavily populated areas and even into rivers that flow through major metropolises. Here is a map of the longest rivers on each continent and some of the most monstrous fish to swim in those waters. Jeremy has already cast his line upon the waters of several of them and encountered a sensational sampling of fierce fish. But who knows how many other dangerous denizens of the deep may be lurking there?

· SOUTH AMERICA ·
NUMBER · 1
AMAZON
LENGTH:
4,000 MILES

SOUTH AMERICA

According to Jeremy, the Amazon is the refuge for the world's most terrifying collection of river monsters. From petite but predatory piranha to enormous leaping Arapaima to killer catfish of every size, the Amazon has no shortage of fearsome fish.

· ANTARCTICA ·
NUMBER · 1
ONYX
LENGTH:
12 MILES

THROUGH IT

The Volga flows through central Russia and harbors monstrous-size Beluga Sturgeon, the largest of which reportedly measured 24 feet in length and weighed in at more than 3,000 pounds!

·EUROPE·
NUMBER·1
VOLGA
LENGTH: 2,290 MILES

·ASIA·
NUMBER·1
YANGTZE RIVER
LENGTH: 3,915 MILES

ASIA

·AFRICA·
NUMBER·1
NILE
LENGTH: 4,132 MILES

The elusive Chinese Paddlefish swims the waters of China's Yangtze River. One of the largest river monsters in the world, the Chinese Paddlefish can reportedly grow up to 23 feet long and weigh 1,000 pounds!

The Nile is home to more than 100 species of freshwater fish, including the Nile Perch, which can grow up to 7 feet long and weigh as much as 250 pounds.

AUSTRALIA

·AUSTRALIA·
NUMBER·1
MURRAY-DARLING
LENGTH: 2,130 MILES

ANTARCTICA
(not shown)

No fish live in this river, which appears only briefly each year during the Antarctic summer when snow and ice melt to form it!

Australia's largest freshwater fish, the Murray Cod, swims in this river. The largest one on record was more than 6 feet long and weighed about 250 pounds.

SILENT ASSASSIN

A 12-year-old girl died in her mother's arms after being suddenly attacked and dealt a deadly knifelike wound by something in the Paraná River while she was playing in the water. Jeremy quickly figured out that the evidence from the death—the shallow water, piercing barb, and speed of attack—all suggested a stingray as the suspect.

Having previously battled to catch a Giant Freshwater Stingray in Thailand, Jeremy knew how difficult and grueling a challenge he faced. Stingrays can grow very large and they tend to hug the bottom of the rivers in which they live. Jeremy has described the experience of reeling in a stingray as being like pulling a plug out and up from the river bottom!

But before the tug of war with a fish bigger than him could even begin, Jeremy found his bait eaten time and time again by hungry piranhas. The Paraná River is home to a chunky piranha species similar to the Red-Bellied Piranha that lives in the Amazon River.

After two weeks without a nibble from a stingray, Jeremy finally landed a small one, which he hauled to the shore for a closer look. He discovered why this fish is called the Short-Tailed Freshwater Stingray—its tail is much shorter than that of other stingrays and it operates more like a deadly dagger than a sharp whip.

Determined to hook a bigger fish, Jeremy cast out his rods in yet another location on the river. He soon found himself locked in combat with a mighty monster, whose pulling force had Jeremy's rod nearly bent double and Jeremy's muscles stretched to their limits. With his back and arms burning, Jeremy held firm for three hours, his longest battle ever, before he successfully brought his worthy otherworldly opponent to shore.

RIVER STINGRAY

Jeremy journeyed for the first time to the remote northeast corner of Argentina to the Paraná River and to the outback town of Bella Vista, 500 miles from where the river empties out into the Atlantic Ocean, to capture a river monster he had never even heard of before. Amazingly, one of the largest and most lethal freshwater fish in the world had managed to swim under his radar!

"WHAT REALLY MAKES THIS MONSTER DIFFERENT IS THAT IT HAS KILLED."

"IT IS A KILLER WITH A WEAPON AS BRUTAL AS A MEDIEVAL MACE, LIKE A CLUB FORTIFIED WITH RUSTY NAILS THAT IT DRIVES IN WITH ITS MASSIVE BULK."

THE BUSINESS END

A stingray's mouth is on its underside and poses no harm to people. The fish's deadly power is in its treacherous tail, which includes a several-inches-long serrated spike that rips through flesh when it thrusts in and again when it pulls out. And if that's not dangerous enough, the barb is coated with mucus that is loaded with bacteria, which can cause infections deep within a person's body, if the toxin that's also in the mucus doesn't manage to kill first! One fisherman Jeremy encountered in Argentina said his wound from a stingray barb took almost seven years to heal. And he was one of the lucky ones.

Is there any good news? Yes: A stingray will usually not attack unless it feels threatened.

FISH FACTS

LENGTH: Up to 5 feet
WEIGHT: More than 450 pounds

Jeremy's largest catch had a wingspan of nearly 4.4 feet and weighed an estimated 250 pounds. With its flattened body and winglike fins, a stingray may look like a watery flying saucer, but it is actually a member of the shark family. The species Jeremy found in the Paraná River had a patterning on its back that allowed it to blend into the water and be almost invisible—and more potentially dangerous to the unsuspecting.

LOCAL LORE

The people of Bella Vista call the Short-Tailed River Stingray "Chucho de Rio," which means "river dog." The fish has such a fearsome reputation that the local fishermen refuse to fish for them even though a single catch could feed many people.

"THERE ARE KILLERS OF ALL SIZES PATROLLING THIS RIVER"

THE DEADLIEST

 Many freshwater fish are suspected of being ruthless killing machines, thanks in part to local stories and legends that derive from the fishes' looks and behavior. In most instances, the suspects are found to be innocent. But when they are proven to be guilty, that's when Jeremy's background as a biologist draws him in for a closer look. He's determined to find out why and how humans can end up on a river monster's menu.

Here are some of the deadliest fish ever to dangle from the end of Jeremy's hook!

NUMBER 1

DEATH BY A THOUSAND CUTS

PIRANHAS

FISH FACTS

Black Piranha
LENGTH: Up to 2 feet
WEIGHT: More than 7 pounds
Red-Bellied Piranha
LENGTH: Up to 1 foot
WEIGHT: Up to 2 pounds

THIS WILL HOOK YOU

More than 30 years ago a bus crashed into a tributary of the Amazon River, and 39 people died. Only a handful of people escaped. One body was found literally stripped of all flesh. The amount of disfigurement on most of the bodies made it challenging for them to be identified.

Only a few of the many species of piranhas are carnivorous but they are such fierce flesh-eaters, known to devour other piranhas and even people, that their ravenous reputation has spread to all the fish in the family. Jeremy encountered the Black Piranha, the largest of the piranha species. Individual piranhas will also take a bite out of people at nesting time. He also witnessed a group of Red-Bellied Piranhas on a feeding frenzy. Attracted by the noise of a creature flailing in the river, a swarm of the fish quickly arrived when Jeremy dangled a freshly killed duck from the market in the water. In a matter of minutes the fish disemboweled the duck.

SUBURBAN STALKER

BULL SHARK

NUMBER 2

Very often a deadly predator will be patrolling the freshwater in an area heavily populated by people. That's the case with the Bull Shark, a fish normally found in the ocean but which has also adapted to life in lakes and the Brisbane River in Australia. Fishing in the middle of the night with a broken finger, Jeremy first hooked a hulking but harmless Queensland Grouper. After three weeks of fishing, working with a team of researchers, Jeremy finally snared a big Bull Shark that wrestled with him for nearly three hours.

What are Bull Sharks doing in the Brisbane River? Researchers think that instead of chasing down their dinner, they save energy by shadowing fishing boats and snatching easy meals off anglers' lines. So these fish are not only lethal, they're also lazy!

FISH FACTS

LENGTH: Up to 11 feet
WEIGHT: Up to 700 pounds

THIS WILL HOOK YOU

When the Brisbane River overflowed and flooded the town of Goodna, two Bull Sharks were suddenly swimming through a shopping center!

GIANT SNAKEHEAD
ARMED COMBAT

Sometimes the quest for a river monster can be just as deadly as the monster itself. Jeremy discovered this when he went searching for the Giant Snakehead in the cloudy waters of the River Kwai in Thailand along with a local fishermen and a homemade spear gun!

In the nearly <u>opaque</u> water, Jeremy strained to see. Would a jaw-snapping snakehead suddenly seize him or would he find himself accidentally impaled on a speeding spear? Luckily for Jeremy he managed to stay safe and to spear a Giant Snakehead as well. And, in a much welcomed surprise, the spear did little more than anger the fish, who was returned with no harm to the river.

Jeremy Wade and Sombat look at a speargun in Thailand.

FISH FACTS

LENGTH: Up to 4 feet
WEIGHT: More than 40 pounds

THIS WILL HOOK YOU

Not every fisherman survives an encounter with this compact carnivore. One man reportedly speared a snakehead, but the fish kept moving forward. It swam right into the fisherman, shoving the end of the metal spear into the man's head, piercing his entire skull!

AFRICAN KILLER

Jeremy describes the Goliath Tiger Fish as having "the combined strength, speed, and ferocity of all the river monsters I've ever encountered." He traveled deep into the heart of Africa to fish for this powerful predator in the Congo River. Proving itself to be a fish that lives up to its tough reputation, Jeremy found himself with ripped and punctured bait time and again until, at last, he hooked a most impressive individual.

GOLIATH TIGER FISH

FISH FACTS

LENGTH: Up to 6 feet
WEIGHT: Up to 100 pounds

THIS WILL HOOK YOU

The jaw on this fish opens wide enough to allow it to bite human-size prey with its razor-sharp teeth that interlock like scissors.

GIANT SALAM

"IT'S A HIDEOUS SCARY GREMLIN."

COLD-BLOODED HORROR

Jeremy quickly realized that the webbed wonder of legend that lives in clear, cold bodies of freshwater, allegedly lying in wait to attack unsuspecting victims, wasn't a fish at all. Instead, as confirmed by a professor from Kyoto University, the animal in question was a Japanese Giant Salamander, an amphibian known in myths and folklore for centuries as the Kappa.

Jeremy traveled into the remote forest hills of Japan to join a research scientist and to try to catch one of these rarely seen salamanders, called "Hanzaki" by the locals. He donned a wet suit and snorkeling gear, along with bite-proof gloves and, after seeing plenty of fish in the water, finally hit the jackpot. He spotted the tail of a salamander sticking out from under a rock in the water. Not a monster to be reeled in with fishing gear, Jeremy instead grabbed hold of the struggling Hanzaki and with a firm grip pulled it up for a closer look.

ANDER

x

Determined to track down the country's most legendary river monsters, Jeremy traveled to Japan and immediately began gathering information at the Tokyo fish market, one of the largest fish markets in the world. About 500,000 tons of fish and seafood pass through the market every year, and the fishermen and merchants have heard of innumerable incredible encounters with monsters, including a creature with webbed feet and a tail that reportedly lives in swamps.

Jeremy standing in front of a busy pedestrian Shibuya Crossing, Tokyo.

ANIMAL INFO

LENGTH: Almost 5 feet
WEIGHT: Up to 65 pounds
Jeremy's catch was about 3 feet long and it weighed nearly 10 pounds. The Japanese and Chinese Giant Salamanders are the two largest species of salamander in the world. But only a few pockets of the Japanese Giant Salamander, which is endangered, still exist in the wild.

"JAPAN'S MOST INFAMOUS RIVER MONSTER HAS BEEN ACCUSED OF HORRIFYING CRIMES FOR CENTURIES."

THE BUSINESS END

This muscular giant with its flat head, wide mouth, and powerful jaws can inflict a brutal bite mark when it is disturbed. It may look stocky and slow but the Japanese Giant Salamander can snatch a fish and suck it down in an instant. This style of feeding has no doubt contributed to the centuries-old legend that this animal sucks out the souls of its victims.

—Jeremy grappling with a salamander in Kamo River.

Jeremy in Kyoto.

Jeremy talking with a monk at Kappabashi Temple, Tokyo.

CULTURE CONNECTION

The Kappa has loomed large in the minds and imaginations of a portion of the Japanese population for centuries. It is feared as a creature strong enough to kill cattle or horses, but it is believed to prefer children. It is reputed to drown its victims and suck spirits out of them.

Jeremy visited a shrine that to this day is dedicated to the sinister river monster. It is a place where people make offerings to the Kappa in the hopes that it will stay away from their children. At the shrine, the Kappa is drawn on the wall as a humanoid figure with four limbs and three claws on each limb. The animal is also depicted with fishlike scales and a beaklike mouth. The offerings people leave include books, sake, water, and all sorts of drawings.

In the south of Japan, on the island of Kyushu, there is a mummified Kappa that was found about 50 years ago inside a box in a brewery.

The mummy is believed to be about 400 years old, which means it dates back to the Edo period in Japan, a time when superstitions and fantasies were commonplace. Today, the mummified creature is on display in the brewery, and many locals still believe that by honoring the Kappa in this way it is, in turn, protecting the brewery from any harm.

"THE JAPANESE AS A NATION ARE JUST OBSESSED BY FISH."

THE MOST BIZARRE

In the unlikely event Jeremy ever needs a reminder that rivers harbor a mind-boggling array of weird and wacky creatures, all he needs to do is revisit his encounters with some of the world's most bizarre freshwater fish.

NUMBER 1

SWALLOWED ALIVE
PIRAIBA

The mouth of the largest member of the catfish family can open more than 2 feet. That's wide enough to swallow a fully grown person. On a fishing trip to the Amazon River in South America, Jeremy caught a man-size Piraiba that growled and thrashed until it was released.

FISH FACTS

LENGTH: About 9.5 feet
WEIGHT: About 440 pounds

THIS WILL HOOK YOU

Jeremy had heard stories of a Piraiba that was found dead with a dead man stuck in its throat. After catching one of the powerful predators for himself, Jeremy was convinced the fish could have bitten off more than it could chew—literally.

SILVER CARP
ALIEN SWARM

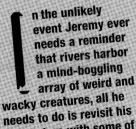

NUMBER 2

If you take a motorboat ride on the Illinois River, prepare to duck! The mere sound of the motor is enough to provoke the Silver Carp in the river to leap out of the water and thrash in the air. The freaky phenomenon is the closest thing to "raining fish" that Jeremy ever experienced.

FISH FACTS

LENGTH: About 3.5 feet
WEIGHT: Up to 100 pounds

THIS WILL HOOK YOU

Silver Carp were introduced into the Illinois River from China about 40 years ago. Today the fish are so plentiful that there are about 13 tons of them for every mile of the river!

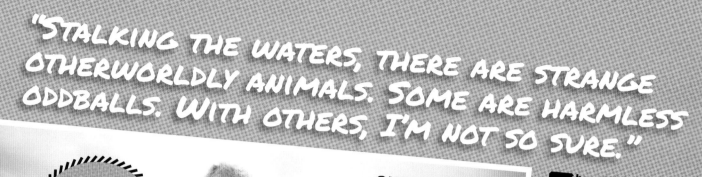

"STALKING THE WATERS, THERE ARE STRANGE OTHERWORLDLY ANIMALS. SOME ARE HARMLESS ODDBALLS. WITH OTHERS, I'M NOT SO SURE."

NUMBER 3

SUPER STRONG RED-TAIL CATFISH

NUMBER 4

ALLIGATOR GAR PUBLIC ENEMY NO. 1

Its snout makes it resemble an alligator so much so that the Alligator Gar was not only named for the deadly reptile, but it was also accused of attacks on people actually committed by alligators on the Trinity River in Texas in the 1930s. The government created a device that shocked and killed the Alligator Gar and brought it to the brink of extinction. But eventually it became clear that the Alligator Gar only eats what it can swallow whole and its mouth is far too small to swallow a human being. Now that its name has been cleared and its reputation restored, wildlife authorities are putting a protection plan in place for the remaining population of this fish.

The catfish species swimming in the Amazon River is part of a varied and diverse family of bizarre beasts. From the strong, super-size Red-Tail Catfish to the diminutive Candiru Asu, Amazon catfish can create memories that last a lifetime, and not good ones. The Candiru Asu, for instance, is a voracious flesh-eater that invades dead or dying animals by cutting a small circular hole through the victim's skin. Then it devours the innards. More than 100 of these munching monsters were found inside one corpse!

FISH FACTS

Candiru Asu
LENGTH: Up to 6 inches

Red-Tail Catfish
LENGTH: Up to 4.5 feet
WEIGHT: Up to 100 pounds

THIS WILL HOOK YOU

How do these tiny little fish create such a big mess? Once they sink their teeth into flesh or an internal organ, they twist off mouthfuls by spinning their bodies!

FISH FACTS

LENGTH: Up to 10 feet
WEIGHT: Up to 365 pounds

THIS WILL HOOK YOU

For Jeremy, the strangest thing about this fish is that, unlike most fish, the Alligator Gar surfaces to breathe air!

ELECTRIC EEL

ELECTRIC EXECUTIONER

"POSSIBLY THE STRANGEST MONSTER CATCH OF MY CAREER."

LOCATION:
BRAZIL, SOUTH AMERICA

Jeremy had long considered Brazil to be his "second home," where he did most of his fishing and where he caught all manner of freshwater killers. But he hadn't been to the Para state, the rugged frontier of cowboy country that is Brazil's wild west. It's an area that outsiders rarely visit, but Jeremy found himself drawn there to investigate a chilling story about a river monster that committed a triple homicide!

Jeremy traveled by boat along the Tocantins River in Brazil to interview an eyewitness to the deaths of three cowboys that occurred in the same spot on the same day. Unfamiliar with what monsters might be lurking in the river water down below, he began fishing immediately. First he caught a Black Piranha, which at 1.5 feet and 2 pounds is the largest piranha species. Next he hooked his first Spotted River Ray, which he dragged to shore to examine its venomous 5-inch-long spiked tail.

For the last leg of his journey Jeremy drove across the country to just outside the small town of El Dorado, where the deaths took place. Ranchers and gold prospectors had cleared the whole area decades earlier. They chased out or killed all the wildlife to make the land safe for livestock and humans. But, clearly, at least one river monster had managed to survive.

The eyewitness told Jeremy that the deaths occurred during the wet season when the pastures of farmland were flooded.

A mule had become stuck in the water and three cowboys went in on their horses to rescue it. Something spooked the horses. They threw the cowboys, who disappeared in three or four feet of water, never to be seen alive again. When the bodies were recovered the next day, they had no marks on them, which made Jeremy rule out both piranhas and stingrays. But they did leave behind a telltale sign: all three had their hands clenched, as if in spasm from a large electric shock. This confirmed what the eyewitness had told Jeremy—the killer was the Electric Eel.

Jeremy first tried to catch one of these electric executioners using a nylon line, which would not conduct electricity. He also donned a thick pair of rubber boots and gloves in order to handle the eel without getting shocked. But all he hooked was a huge Red-Tail Catfish. Several attempts to catch an Electric Eel by fishing with a bamboo rod as the locals do were not successful either.

Jeremy's final attempt to catch an Electric Eel found him in an area southwest of Marabá, at a tiny muddy pool right in a middle of a cattle pasture! Using a lasso, a fitting piece of equipment in cowboy country, he managed to get an eel to go through the noose. He pulled the killer creature into a mud trench where he figured out it was nearly 6 feet long! As he slid the fish back into the little pool of water, barely 6 inches deep, he realized that there were close to 20 eels, mostly smaller in size, weaving in and out of the roots of a tree in the water. A most shocking find in the most unlikely of places!

"THIS IS A NEW KILLER FOR ME."

THE BUSINESS END

The back four-fifths of the fish is where the zapping power is located and the electricity is produced by specially adapted muscles. Every few seconds an Electric Eel emits an electric pulse to survey its surroundings. At about 10 volts a pulse, the charge is small and harmless. But you don't want to touch this eel or be touched by it if it is in attack or defense mode. Then it is capable of producing 400 to 600 volts, which is almost as much electricity as a heart defibrillator produces! The jarring jolt can cause a person's heart to stop.

FISH FACTS

LENGTH: More than 8 feet
WEIGHT: Over 40 pounds
Despite its name, the Electric Eel is not an eel at all but is a member of the knife fish family, a family that compensates for poor eyesight by producing electric fields that help them navigate and communicate. Only the Electric Eel can produce enough of a charge to shock or kill a human being.

LOCAL LORE

According to a legend told by Brazil's indigenous Tupi people before electricity was understood, a warrior carelessly dropped a lightning bolt on an eel, giving the fish its mysterious power. Today the Electric Eel is know locally as the "Poraqué," or "the one who sends you to sleep."

GOING TRIBAL

"I HAVE PLUNGED DEEP INTO A CULTURE THAT HAS LIVED IN BALANCE WITH THE OCEAN FOR MILLENNIA."

One of Jeremy's most extreme adventures ever, which took him to the remote wilderness of the Solomon Islands in the South Pacific, was not to pursue any specific fish but to learn the ancient, simple fishing methods used by the local people.

Jeremy was granted permission to live for three weeks with the Vahole people, a tribe with a staggering array of fishing techniques. Many of their fishing methods are found nowhere else in the world. The Vahole, who live in primitive housing with no electricity, fish as a matter of survival. They must catch fish in order to have enough to eat and they don't catch more than the tribe needs for that day. As far as Jeremy is concerned, the Vahole have "a good claim to be the world's most expert fishermen."

GETTING HIS FEET WET

Jeremy showed his fishing tackle and photos of some of the river monsters he'd caught to the Vahole in an attempt to win their acceptance and trust. But he still had to be initiated in the tribal ways of fishing. His first expedition was with the women, hunting for clams in the mud!

THE VINE INTERVENTION

Next, Jeremy worked with the entire village, wielding machetes to hack through jungle vines, which were then wound together to form an enormous floating chain. Fish drawn into the huge circle for some inexplicable reason won't swim under or cross the vine barrier, even though it isn't a net. Tribespeople spear the fish that try to break through. Jeremy managed to win a measure of respect from the Vahole by spearing several fish in the enclosure, which was no easy feat due to the small size and fast movement of his targets.

"HALF FISHING, HALF MAGIC, THESE ANCIENT TECHNIQUES ARE ON THE BRINK OF EXTINCTION. AND I WANT TO LEARN WHAT I CAN BEFORE THEY ARE GONE AND LOST BENEATH THE WAVES FOREVER."

ENTANGLED IN A WEB

Jeremy was privileged to be the first "outsider" to be shown and be part of an ancient, ingenious fishing technique that only two men in the Solomon Islands know how to practice today. He caught a fish using just a few banana leaves and a spider web! The leaves are stitched together to form a kite. The web is not only the string, but it also skips against the water as the kite moves, attracting needlefish. The needlefish's teeth work like a fishhook—they get tangled in the fine sticky mesh of the web.

TAKING AIM

Another tribesman showed Jeremy the ancient art of fishing with a bow and arrow. It was a challenge trying to hit a small fast-moving fish while standing in a wobbly canoe but Jeremy managed to catch a fish to contribute to the communal dinner.

HOLDING THE LINE

Finally Jeremy was allowed to try handline fishing. In handline fishing you bait the end of a hook attached to the line and then hold the line with your hands. There is no rod and the line can cut deeply into a person's hands. But Jeremy was not to be deterred because his quarry was none other than a shark! He was allowed to fish in a lagoon that contained a shark sacred to the Vahole, a shark believed to be a defender of the entire tribe. After the shark bit through the wire and took not only the bait but the hook as well, Jeremy's guide went to speak to the shark. He explained to the fish that Jeremy was not there to harm him but would let him go again. And shortly thereafter Jeremy hooked the shark! After a long, exhausting, relentless duel, the shark finally tired enough for Jeremy to haul it into his canoe and get a good look at him. Using such a simple device Jeremy had caught a powerful 80-pound Gray Reef Shark!

FISHING FOR

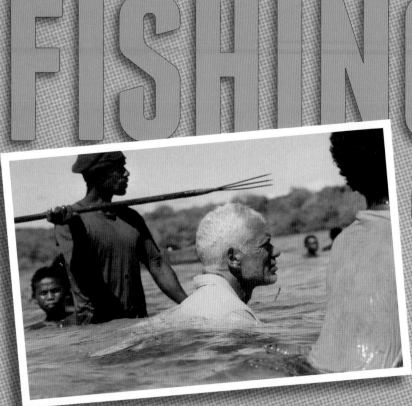

Jeremy is all about fishing for answers that solve the mysteries surrounding the world's freshwater fish. And he's also quite open about answering questions posed by fans and fishing enthusiasts.

Q. DO YOU ACTUALLY FIND COMFORT IN THE ENVIRONMENTS YOU TRAVEL TO?

A. Yes, very much so. I think it's something that is often overlooked—that fishing is not just about the fish; it's an experience. And even a day without catching a fish is a day well spent. Although I think if you're fishing and you're well prepared, you always have a sense that something could happen at any moment, so the time doesn't drag. Fishing makes you be still in the landscape. You see things and experience things in a different way than you would otherwise.

Q. HOW DEVASTATING DO YOU THINK THE TSUNAMI WAS TO THE FRESHWATER CREATURES YOU CAUGHT IN JAPAN [BEFORE THE EARTHQUAKE AND TSUNAMI IN 2011] AND TO THEIR ENVIRONMENT?

A. The main place that we were was actually up in the mountains, so I'm not sure that the tsunami would have had any impact on the creatures we filmed. But I think more generally what the tsunami did—a lot of seawater came on land—could have been fairly devastating to any fish in more lowland rivers. Seawater being dumped on them would probably have killed a lot of freshwater fish.

Q. WHAT MAJOR CHANGES DO YOU THINK THE WORLD NEEDS TO MAKE TO PROTECT THE GREAT MONSTERS YOU'VE CAUGHT?

A. I believe it begins with an awareness of their existence. And I think it's true to say that before *River Monsters* started, a lot of people had no idea that these things even existed. You have to know that the monsters exist before you care about them. And what that should do is lead people to care about the environment the creatures thrive in.

Q. YOUR SUCCESS COMES CLEARLY IN PART BECAUSE OF YOUR ABILITY TO GET INTO THE MIND OF THE FISH YOU'RE SEEKING. HOW DID YOU LEARN TO DO THIS?

A. I suppose it's about imagining yourself under the water. Fish see the world very differently from us. We're very much dominated by vision, and vision does play a part underwater. But in rivers where visibility is not good, fish rely on vibration, smell, and maybe even electrical currents. So it makes you think in a different way. The fascinating thing about rivers is that the water is moving—and it's not moving in a straightforward way. For fish, it's about feeling secure,

ANSWERS

but also about finding food. So if you were a fish, where would you be? That's always the first question.

Q. HOW DO YOU WORK ON FISHING AS A SKILL? DO YOU TRAIN?

A. It can be physically demanding. With some fishing, you're constantly casting and retrieving in a very energetic way—you've got to be quite fit for that. But no, I don't train much specifically. I do keep myself fit—I tend to use stairs instead of elevators. I don't lift weights but I do a bit of yoga, running, and occasionally, a bit of aikido. Some fishing is quite physically demanding. If you've got a heavy fish—something like a stingray or a shark—it's not so much about letting that fish run around and tire itself out. You really are just trying to drag it in on heavy gear, so that's pretty physical. Also, the environments are quite punishing—just living in a tropical environment keeps you fit. You're sweating a lot; you're having to carry bags around. I suppose sometimes accurate casting is a thing, particularly with lure fishing, but again, I tend to do that on the job rather than practice in between fishing trips.

Q. IS THERE A TRIP THAT YOU'D NEVER WANT TO REPEAT?

A. I used to think that about the Congo. I made a couple of trips to the Congo and caught nothing, and you come back and you think, "I never want to do that again." But the fact that I didn't

catch anything meant unfinished business; I've got to go back. And again, although I didn't catch anything, I learned something. I'm now one step closer to what I wanted. So, yes, the Congo; part of me didn't want to go back but part of me knew that I had to go back and get the Goliath Tigerfish.

SURINAME, SOUTH AMERICA

Situated on South America's northeast coast, Suriname is the continent's smallest country, with a total population of only 500,000 people. It boasts one of the largest contiguous areas of unspoiled rain forest in the world. Jeremy traveled deep into the heart of the country, far removed from civilization, in search of a river monster with an enormous reputation for ferocity.

THE BUSINESS END

The Wolf Fish, named for its wolflike teeth, has a mouth loaded with more than 100 spiky fangs. That's about four times more teeth than a piranha has! And, unlike a piranha, when it bites flesh, the Wolf Fish often clings to its victim like a dog with a bone, inflicting a deep, painful bite mark.

WOLF FISH
JUNGLE KILLER

"HAVING THE WEAPONRY IS ONE THING. HAVING THE ATTITUDE IS QUITE ANOTHER— THE WOLF FISH IS EQUIPPED WITH BOTH."

Jeremy traveled deep into Suriname's wild interior in search of the predatory Anjumara, also known as the Wolf Fish. After trekking through miles of tangled rain forest with its oppressive heat and humidity, Jeremy began to fish in the Courentyne River. At 450 miles long, the Courentyne, with its frequent crushing rapids and deep turbulent pools, is Suriname's longest river, but much of it remains unexplored.

Over the course of three weeks, Jeremy reeled in Black Piranhas and Red-Tail Catfish and successfully evaded the ever-present killer caiman in the river, but he failed to hook a Wolf Fish. As Jeremy's time began to run out, at last he landed a sizable Wolf Fish.

FISH FACTS

LENGTH: Up to 4.5 feet
WEIGHT: Up to 80 pounds
Unlike many other river monsters, the Wolf Fish frequents shallow instead of deep river water.

ALASKA

Sockeye Salmon

CANADA

NUMBER 3

NUMBER 1

Northern Pike

NUMBER 6

WASHINGTON

OREGON

NUMBER 7

JEREMY'S TOP 10 RIVERS TO FISH IN NORTH AMERICA

Jeremy Wade chose these North American rivers as the top 10 spots to visit if you're angling to catch—and release—your own freshwater monster.

1 Rivers near Kvichak River, Alaska: The Kvichak River in southwestern Alaska has the world's biggest run of Sockeye Salmon up into Lake Iliamna and beyond.

2 Florida Canals: Today, thousands of miles of canals and their water-control structures are carved into Florida's landscape, especially in the southeastern part of the state. They contain more than 30 nonnative fish species (at the last count), including the Peacock Bass from the Amazon and the invasive Bullseye Snakehead, a predator with a fierce reputation from Southeast Asia.

3 Lake Clark, Alaska: Located in Southern Alaska, it holds good-size Northern Pike.

4 Illinois River, Illinois: Sometimes you don't need a rod and line to catch fish here. The Asian Silver Carp is an introduced species that jumps right into your boat.

5 Trinity River, Texas: This 710 mile-long river that flows entirely within the state is home to the dinosaur-like Alligator Gar.

Asian Silver Carp

NUMBER **8**

NUMBER **4**

NUMBER **9**

NEW YORK

MONTANA

WYOMING

ILLINOIS

TEXAS

FLORIDA

NUMBER **2**

NUMBER **5**

Bullseye Snakehead

6 Columbia River, Oregon-Washington: The largest river in the Pacific Northwest region of North America has spectacular scenery and is a shining example of how decimated fish stocks can be rescued by enlightened fisheries management.

7 Snake River, Wyoming: Beautiful, hard-fighting, cutthroat trout can be caught within this river's magnificent and awe-inspiring scenery.

8 Yellowstone River, Montana: The longest undammed river in the lower 48 states is considered to be one of the great Rainbow Trout streams of the world.

9 Hudson River, New York: This river rises at Lake Tear of the Clouds on the slopes of Mount Marcy in the Adirondack Mountains, flows past Albany, and finally forms the border between New York City and New Jersey at its mouth before emptying into Upper New York Bay. You never know, catching a fish from an unexpected place is sometimes more rewarding than catching one from a place where many others have caught them before.

NUMBER **10** The river near you: Sometimes big fish can be right under your nose. Fishing is about making your own discoveries!

49

LOCATION:
AUSTRALIA

Jeremy headed to the Fitzroy River in Australia's wild northwest, one of the last strongholds of the rapidly disappearing freshwater Sawfish.

Nearly 20 years ago, on Jeremy's very first fishing trip to the Amazon, he was in a hardware store looking for rope and other supplies when he came across a rostrum, or snout, of a river monster the locals called "Araguagua." It was a Sawfish. Jeremy had no idea that this fish, armed with a chainsaw-like snout, could swim from its usual home in the sea far inland up rivers. In the years that followed he heard several accounts of this fish attacking fishermen and hacking their boats in half in rivers around the globe. He decided it was time to get a firsthand look at this perilous predator and headed off to Australia, one of the few places the creature still swims today.

Jeremy headed to a deep channel known as Telegraph Pool, a lower section of the Fitzroy River. Strong tides wash smaller fish into the area, making it a rich hunting ground for large predators like the Sawfish, and also for Barramundi, a sport fish with a fighting spirit that many locals catch. Because the freshwater Sawfish is endangered, Jeremy was granted special permission to try to catch and release the sharp snouted fish. After spending the entire night without a nibble, Jeremy found another fisherman who had accidentally hooked a 2-foot Sawfish pup. Jeremy estimated that the fish's size made it about 1 year old and that meant that breeding-size adults had to be in the area.

After an unsuccessful attempt at net fishing with an elder of the Aborigines followed by hours of fruitlessly fishing in another location with nothing but a handline with a hook and bit of lead holding the bait in place, Jeremy traveled back downstream to join a Sawfish research scientist and his team. In the dark, murky crocodile-infested waters at night, Jeremy reeled in a bull shark. It was an unexpected and exciting catch—it's unusual for a bull shark, which is normally an ocean fish, to be so far upstream in freshwater.

But his time to catch a Sawfish was running out. Jeremy returned to fish at the exact spot he had seen the Sawfish pup. "Fish on! Fish on!" he cried in response to a strong tug on the line. And there, finally, was the full-grown Sawfish he had waited 20 years to catch.

WFISH CHAINSAW PREDATOR

Jeremy and a local fisherman holding a Sawfish on the Fitzroy River.

"AT LAST, THE ANIMAL THAT HAS BEEN SWIMMING AROUND IN MY HEAD FOR ALMOST 20 YEARS!"

THE BUSINESS END

There's no mistaking which end of this fish demands respect. The largest Sawfish Jeremy caught was nearly 7 feet long, 1.5 feet of which was the fish's snout. Thirty-nine needle-sharp teeth, each about 1 inch long, lined either side of the rostrum. Rostrum teeth can be twice that long!

The fully armed Sawfish is ready at an instant to use its rostrum to defend itself from predators like sharks and crocodiles, slashing at adversaries and ripping through flesh. But the rostrum is also packed with sensory cells that detect prey moving along the river bottom. It can function like a shovel and dig up its dinner of small fish and crustaceans. The rostrum may grab everyone's immediate attention, but the mouth of the Sawfish is another amazing instrument of death; it's a monstrous crushing machine, lined with 17,000 small teeth fused together!

There is no proof that a Sawfish will attack a human unless provoked, but according to records Jeremy found, people have used the rostrum to attack each other. Long ago, in places like the Philippines, New Guinea, and New Zealand rostrums were wielded like weapons to slice open the abdomens of enemies. And one slash from a rostrum across the inner elbow is reportedly enough to make a person bleed to death.

FISH FACTS

LENGTH: Up to 20 feet
WEIGHT: Possibly over 2,000 pounds
While it may resemble an aquatic power tool that has often been mistaken for a shark, the distinctive-looking Sawfish is a member of the ray family of fish. Sawfish have been overfished, primarily for their fins, which are considered delicacies in some parts of the world, and all species are listed as endangered.

Research indicates that this fish swims as far as 200 miles upriver to have its babies. The Fitzroy River is a Sawfish nursery!

LOCAL LORE

Australia's indigenous people, the Aborigines, have lived with Sawfish for at least 50,000 years and the predator features prominently in their tribal dances. In one of their dreamtime dances, the animal uses its huge saw to gouge out the rivers of the land.

"I SHUDDER TO IMAGINE THAT RACK OF TEETH SCYTHING INTO HUMAN FLESH."

GO FISH!

1 THE SAWFISH'S SNOUT LOOKS LIKE:
a. a hammer
b. a chainsaw
c. a trumpet
d. a bird beak

2 THE WOLF FISH IS NAMED THAT BECAUSE:
a. It howls at the full moon.
b. It is covered in fur.
c. It has spiky wolflike teeth.
d. It travels in packs like wolves do.

3 THE LONGFIN EEL ATTACKS THIS WAY:
a. It squeezes its victim.
b. It bites its prey.
c. It shocks its prey.
d. both a and c

4 THIS FISH IS SACRED TO THE VAHOLE PEOPLE:
a. guppy
b. piranha
c. parrotfish
d. shark

5 JEREMY TRIED FISHING IN THE SOLOMON ISLANDS USING:
a. a chain of vines
b. a spider web and banana leaves
c. a bow and arrow
d. all of the above

6 THE ELECTRIC EEL PRODUCES ENOUGH ELECTRICITY TO:
a. kill a person
b. just shock a person
c. light up a whole neighborhood
d. be completely harmless

7 HOW DID THE PACU GET FROM SOUTH AMERICA TO PAPUA NEW GUINEA?
a. It hitched a ride.
b. It swam.
c. It took a cruise.
d. It was brought there as a food fish for the local people.

8 JEREMY FINALLY LOCATED AN ELECTRIC EEL IN:
a. the ocean
b. a small pool in a cow pasture
c. the Congo River
d. the Amazon River

9 WHICH AMPHIBIAN DID JEREMY CATCH IN JAPAN?
a. Red-Eyed Tree Frog
b. Wyoming Toad
c. Giant Salamander
d. none of the above

10 WHAT DO SILVER CARP DO THAT IS SURPRISING?
a. They leap out of the water.
b. They sing like birds.
c. They glow in the dark.
d. They eat each other.

River Monsters supports catch and release techniques that help ensure sustainable fisheries for future generations.

QUIZ

If there's one thing you learned from reading this book it's that you have to stay alert and pay close attention when you're around river monsters! Did you stay on your toes enough to learn the answers to the questions below? All the information you need is swimming somewhere in the pages of this book.

11 THE JAPANESE GIANT SALAMANDER IS:
a. abundant
b. rare
c. endangered
d. small

12 WHICH OF THE FOLLOWING DID JEREMY CATCH ON THE CONGO RIVER?
a. a cold
b. a chill
c. a Goliath Tiger Fish
d. an Alligator Gar

13 THE SHORT-TAILED STINGRAY HAS A VENOMOUS:
a. tail
b. nose
c. fin
d. mouth

14 IN ITS MOUTH A SAWFISH HAS:
a. 17,000 teeth
b. 1,700 teeth
c. no teeth at all
d. 17 teeth

15 ONE REASON A SHORT-TAILED STINGRAY IS HARD TO CATCH IS:
a. It hides in rocks.
b. It hugs the bottom of a river.
c. It doesn't like bait.
d. It is too fast.

16 THE LONGEST RIVER IN THE WORLD IS THE:
a. Amazon
b. Danube
c. Congo
d. Nile

17 THIS FISH HIT JEREMY IN THE CHEST!
a. Arapaima
b. Sturgeon
c. Bull Shark
d. none of the above

18 RED-BELLIED PACU ARE COMMONLY FOUND IN THE:
a. Amazon River
b. Courentyne River
c. Volga River
d. Onyx River

19 THE WOLF FISH PREFERS:
a. deep water
b. shallow water
c. soapy water
d. saltwater

20 AN ELECTRIC EEL USUALLY USES ELECTRIC CHARGES TO:
a. Navigate in murky water
b. Keep itself awake
c. Communicate with other fish
d. both a and c

Answers on page 56

GLOSSARY

CONTIGUOUS—connected and unbroken

CRUSTACEAN—an aquatic animal with a hard protective outer shell; includes crab, shrimp, lobsters, and barnacles

DEFIBRILLATOR—a machine that uses electric shocks to help someone experiencing heart distress

HABITAT—the natural environment in which an animal or plant lives

INDIGENOUS—originating in and characteristic of a particular region or country

OFFAL—the edible, internal organs of an animal, including the heart, liver, and tongue

OPAQUE—not see-through; cloudy

ROSTRUM—the snout of a fish such as the Sawfish

VOLT—a unit of electromotive force

ANSWER KEY TO QUIZ ON PAGES 54-55

1. b	6. a	11. c	16. d
2. c	7. d	12. c	17. a
3. b	8. b	13. a	18. a
4. d	9. c	14. a	19. b
5. d	10. a	15. b	20. d

0-5 Correct: As shocking as a jolt from an Electric Eel

6-10 Correct: A Longfin Eel is slithering between your legs

11-17 Correct: All the Wolf Fish around you are nonaggressive

18-20 Correct: Extremely Excellent!